Alba White Wolf lives in the city of Steelfields with her family:
Kay the Carrot Top and her two daddies, Bill the Accountant and
Frank the Postman. Alba White Wolf is a very clever wolf and she
helps Frank the Postman to deliver the post every day.

One day, Frank the Postman came home from work with some exciting news, 'Alba White Wolf and I have been given a special job! We are going to Europe to deliver 27 very important parcels.' 'That sounds fun! Can I come too?' asked Kay the Carrot Top.

'I'm afraid not,' said Bill the Accountant, 'You have to stay home with me and go to your primary school.' Kay the Carrot Top was very disappointed, but Frank the Postman promised that he would send her a postcard from every country he visited with Alba White Wolf.

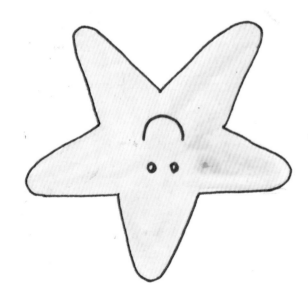

'What's inside the very important parcels?'
asked Kay the Carrot Top.
'Golden stars!' replied Frank the Postman,
'We have to deliver them all before Christmas.'
'Will you make it back home for Christmas day?'
she asked. 'I hope so!' he replied. Then he
kissed her goodbye and set off on his
adventures in Europe with Alba White Wolf.

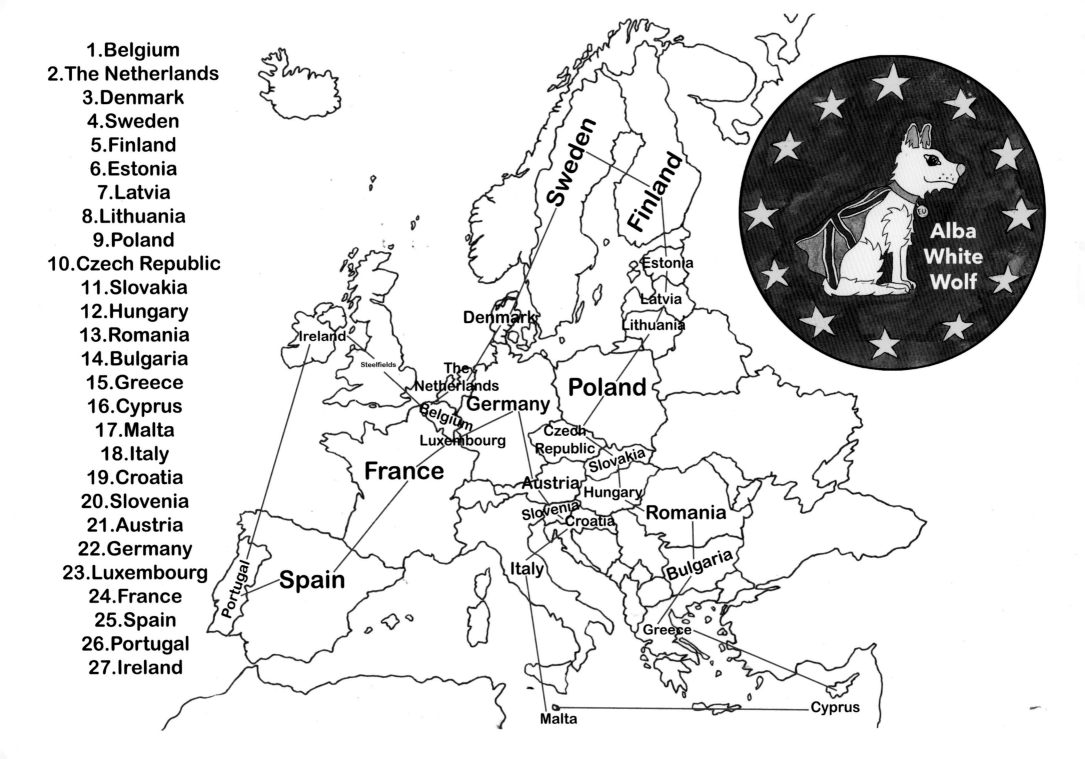

1. Belgium
2. The Netherlands
3. Denmark
4. Sweden
5. Finland
6. Estonia
7. Latvia
8. Lithuania
9. Poland
10. Czech Republic
11. Slovakia
12. Hungary
13. Romania
14. Bulgaria
15. Greece
16. Cyprus
17. Malta
18. Italy
19. Croatia
20. Slovenia
21. Austria
22. Germany
23. Luxembourg
24. France
25. Spain
26. Portugal
27. Ireland

Alba
White
Wolf

We have arrived in Brussels! We drove to Dover in the post van and travelled on the ferry across the Channel to Dunkirk, which is in France. Alba White Wolf was very sea-sick during the crossing. She couldn't sleep all night because she was having nightmares! She is still very scared of water. We drove across the border and on to Brussels, the capital of Belgium, and saw the amazing arch on this postcard! Then we tried some delicious Belgian waffles before delivering the first parcel to the Belgian parliament. They speak 3 languages in Belgium; French, German and Dutch! Alba White Wolf can't woof in any of them!
Frank the Postman &

Kay the Carrot Top
88 Crooked Moor Road
Brush Hill
Steelfields
England
S10 AWW

Arcade du Cinquantenaire, Brussels, Belgium

Our second destination is the Netherlands. The country is very flat, so there are no mountains. The highest point is only 322m. There is a lot of farm land with traditional windmills. They are famous for growing tulips, which make the fields look like rainbows. You will be interested to know that orange carrots came from the Netherlands; before that they were yellow and purple. Imagine if you had purple hair! Lots of people ride bikes in the capital city, Amsterdam. Some parents cycle 'backfiets' which are bikes with wheel barrows at the front for children to ride in! We had a go but Alba White Wolf didn't like being pushed around!

Frank the Postman &

Tulip Farm, the Netherlands

Kay the Carrot Top
88 Crooked Moor Road
Brush Hill
Steelfields
England
S10 AWW

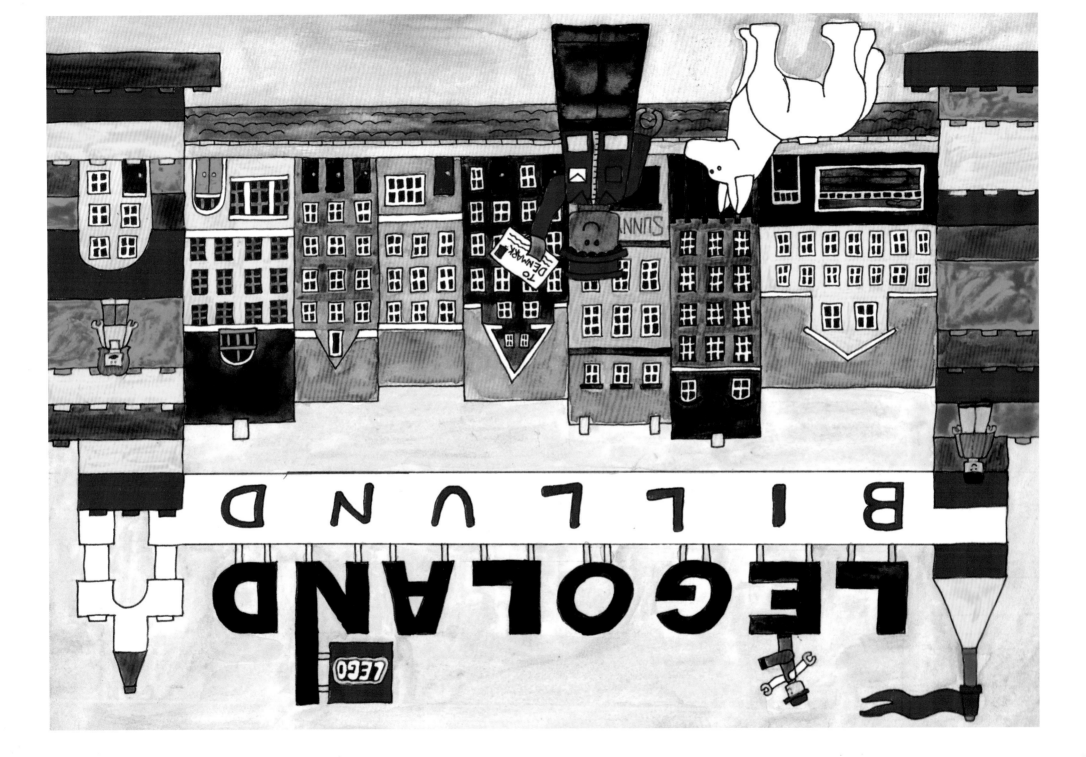

We arrived in Copenhagen, the capital of Denmark, and it was pouring down with rain! So we found a nice coffee shop where we tried a Danish pastry while we waited for the rain to stop. Afterwards we went for a walk down a very long pedestrian street - it's 3.2km with no cars! After we delivered the third parcel, we went shopping and Alba White Wolf found some sweets called 'Hundeprutter' which means 'dog farts'! We will send you some in the post along with a box of Lego which comes from Denmark! The name is short for 'Leg godt' which means 'play well' in Danish!

Frank the Postman &

Legoland Billund, Denmark

Kay the Carrot Top
88 Crooked Moor Road
Brush Hill
Steelfields
England
S10 AWW

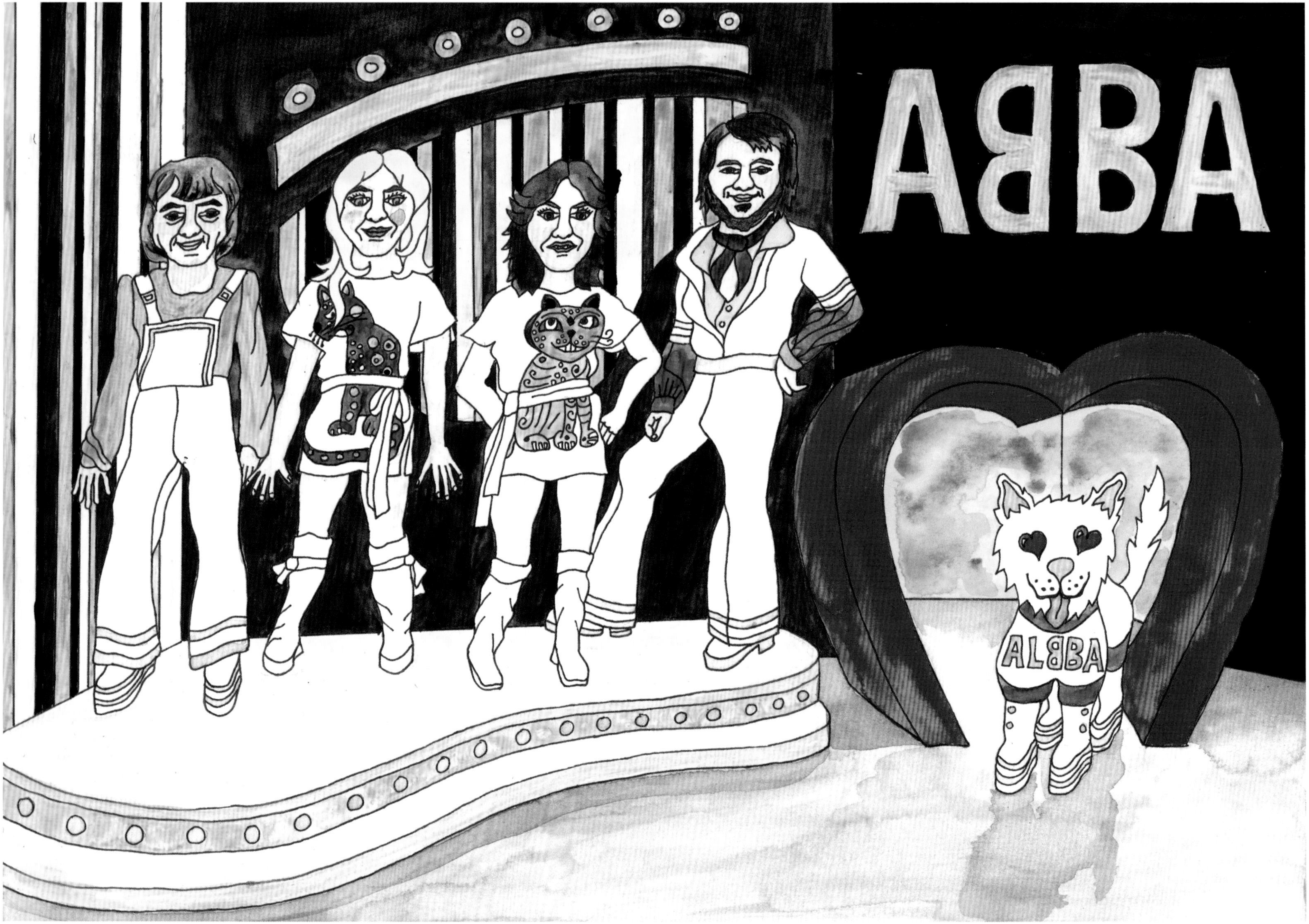
ABBA
ALBBA

Today we drove from Denmark to Sweden across the Oresund Bridge, which is the longest cable-tied road in the world. It was a long drive to the capital city, Stockholm, to deliver the fourth parcel. We visited the ABBA museum whilst we were there because ALBBA White Wolf is a big fan! We bought a CD of their music to listen to in the post van. We're staying in Stockholm tonight before continuing on our travels. We ate Swedish meat balls for dinner and tried some black liquorice flavoured, salmiakki ice-cream! Tomorrow night we are staying in an ice hotel in Jukkasjarvi, in the North of Sweden - How cool is that?

Frank the Postman &

ABBA: The Museum, Stockholm, Sweden

Kay the Carrot Top
88 Crooked Moor Road
Brush Hill
Steelfields
England
S10 AWW

We crossed the border into Lapland which is in the north of Finland and we stayed in an igloo made out of glass! You can see the beautiful Aurora Borealis light up the sky from your bed! We met Santa Claus in Lapland; he was busy in his workshop making gifts for Christmas. He told us we had better hurry up if we want to deliver all the parcels in time! So, we sped off in the post van and headed down south to the capital, Helsinki. We saw a Death Metal band called Lordi who won the 2006 Eurovision Song Contest. I went for a sauna afterwards, but it was too hot for Alba White Wolf, so she ate a smoked reindeer pizza instead! Frank the Postman &

The Aurora Borealis, Lapland, Finland

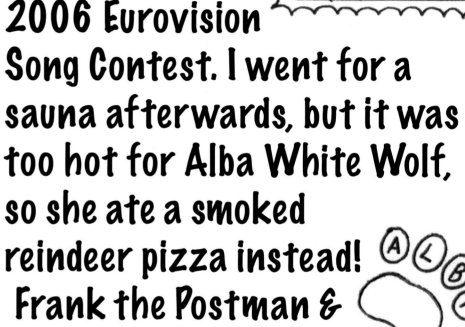

Kay the Carrot Top
88 Crooked Moor Road
Brush Hill
Steelfields
England
S10 AWW

Our sixth destination is Estonia. we took a ferry across the Gulf of Finland to the capital city, Tallinn. They were very pleased when we delivered their parcel. They had been waiting for it to decorate their Christmas tree in the medieval Old Town. They told me Estonians put up the first ever Christmas tree in 1441 - I wonder where Santa Claus left the presents before that? They also drink hot apple cider in the winter so I had a glass before we headed off. Apparently, it's the law to wear a safety reflector if you are walking at night. Luckily, we were driving in the post van, otherwise I might have been arrested because I don't have one!

Frank the Postman &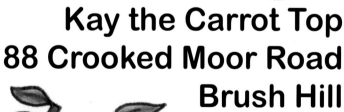

Tallinn Old town, Estonia

Kay the Carrot Top
88 Crooked Moor Road
Brush Hill
Steelfields
England
S10 AWW

Tonight we are staying somewhere exciting and scary - a prison! There is a hotel in an old jail in Karosta, on the west coast of Latvia. I told Alba White Wolf that the police are going to lock her up for chasing the White Wagtail which is the Latvian national bird. I wonder if she'll be angry when she finds out it was just a joke? On the way there we stopped at the capital, Riga, to deliver the seventh parcel. A Latvian man immediately put the star at the top of their tree in the Town Hall Square. 'Don't believe what they say in Estonia! We invented decorating Christmas trees,' he told us. Now I don't know who to believe!

Frank the Postman &

Town Hall Square, Riga, Latvia

Kay the Carrot Top
88 Crooked Moor Road
Brush Hill
Steelfields
England
S10 AWW

After our "stay in prison" we travelled to Vilnius, the capital of Lithuania and delivered our eighth parcel. Lithuanian is the oldest language in Europe, but people also speak Russian and Polish. Basketball is the national sport, so I played a game whilst Alba White Wolf watched. She's better at drooling on her paws than dribbling a basketball! Afterwards, we went up in a hot air balloon over the city. We saw a stork, the national

bird, fly past. I was worried its long beak might puncture our balloon! For dinner we had a bright pink beetroot soup called 'Borscht' and a pie made from mushrooms that we had picked ourselves in the forest!

Frank the Postman &

Trakai Island Castle, Lithuania

Kay the Carrot Top
88 Crooked Moor Road
Brush Hill
Steelfields
England
S10 AWW

We rode on a pirate ship in Gdansk, a city on the north coast of Poland. There weren't any real pirates on board but there were lots of tourists taking photos! We travelled to Warsaw, the capital of Poland, where we delivered the ninth parcel. There was a statue of my favourite composer - Chopin. He wrote wonderful classical music that you call "boring"! We are staying in Wroclaw tonight and eating dinner in an extremely old restaurant which opened in 1273! I had 'Bigos' which means 'hunter's stew' and a bowl of sour cucumber soup! There are lots of funny little dwarves in the city. Alba White Wolf keeps barking at them!

Frank the Postman &

Gdansk Shipyard, Poland

Kay the Carrot Top
88 Crooked Moor Road
Brush Hill
Steelfields
England
S10 AWW

Our tenth European destination is the beautiful city of Prague, the capital of the Czech Republic. Prague Castle is the largest in Europe! You can see it from Charles Bridge, which is a gothic stone structure. There are lots of artists and vendors who sell souvenirs to all the tourists. For dinner, I ate a tasty meal of roast pork, dumplings and sauerkraut which is pickled cabbage! Alba White Wolf had a bowl of garlic soup and now

Charles Bridge, Prague, Czech Republic

her breath smells! We read a famous book called 'Metamorphosis' at bed time. It's about a man who wakes up to discover he has turned into an insect. I hope I haven't grown extra legs in the morning!

Frank the Postman &

Kay the Carrot Top
88 Crooked Moor Road
Brush Hill
Steelfields
England
S01 7HE

Yesterday we went for a lovely walk in the Tatras Mountains that border Poland and Slovakia, our eleventh destination. Alba White Wolf met another wolf - luckily it was friendly! Then we visited a beautiful fairy-tale castle in Bojnice. I wanted to go on a night tour but Alba White Wolf was scared she would see a ghost! I tried a smoked string cheese that comes in a plait; it's called 'Korbáčik' which means 'little whip'.

Tatra Mountains, Slovakia

Today we are travelling to the capital city, Bratislava. We had lunch in a UFO restaurant on a bridge over the Danube River. There were amazing views over the city but sadly no aliens!
Frank the Postman &

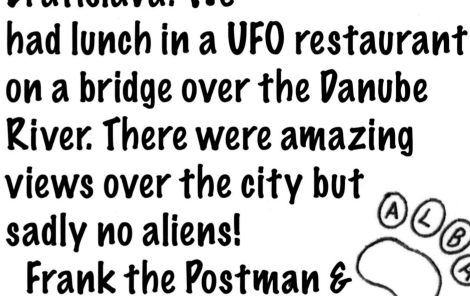

Kay the Carrot Top
88 Crooked Moor Road
Brush Hill
Steelfields
England
S10 AWW

We are now visiting the twelfth European country on our list - Hungary! We are staying in the capital city Budapest, which is actually two cities, Buda and Pest, which are separated by the Danube River! We went to the famous thermal baths and we saw some old men playing chess in their swimming trunks! Alba White Wolf didn't want to get her paws wet, but I enjoyed relaxing in the hot waters after all our travelling! We ate beef goulash for dinner - It was delicious but they put a lot of spicy paprika in their food! Hungarians invented some cool things like biros and Rubik's cubes. I can solve them but Alba White Wolf can't!

Frank the Postman &

Thermal Baths, Budapest, Hungary

Kay the Carrot Top
88 Crooked Moor Road
Brush Hill
Steelfields
England
S10 AWW

We drove down an exciting road called the Transfagarasan in the post van today. It snakes down the Carpathian Mountains in Romania. We delivered the thirteenth parcel to the Palace of Parliament in Bucharest, which is the second biggest building in the world! Last night we stayed in a hotel near Bran Castle which inspired the novel about Count Dracula. I'm not sure if we'll see a vampire, but we have seen a few brown bears on our journey. Apparently, they go into the cities to steal food from the rubbish bins like foxes do in the UK! The fountain pen was invented in Romania; I'm trying to write with one but I keep smudging the ink! Frank the Postman & Alba

Bran Castle, Brasov, Romania

Kay the Carrot Top
88 Crooked Moor Road
Brush Hill
Steelfields
England
S10 AWW

Our fourteenth destination, Bulgaria, has the oldest name of any European country. Its name hasn't changed since 681AD - That's over 1,300 years ago! The national instrument is the gaida, which are bagpipes like the kind in Scotland. We delivered the parcel to the capital city, Sofia, before heading east to the Rose Valley where we are staying. The Rose Valley produces petals for rose oil which is used in most perfumes.

The Rose Valley, Bulgaria

They gave me a special yoghurt that can only be made in Bulgarian air. When they asked me if I liked it, I shook my head! They shake their head to mean yes and nod to mean no, and the yoghurt tasted delicious!
Frank the Postman &

Kay the Carrot Top
88 Crooked Moor Road
Brush Hill
Steelfields
England
S10 AWW

We arrived in Greece today and delivered the fifteenth star to the capital city, Athens. The weather is lovely; they have 250 days of sun per year on average. Lots of the buildings are painted with a bright turquoise paint called Kyanos which is supposed to keep evil away! Around 80% of Greece is mountains and it has about 2000 islands. We are staying in Athens tonight and for dinner we ate Moussaka and a Greek salad.

The Parthenon, Athens, Greece

Greece is thought of as the home of mathematics because of the work of ancient Greek philosophers like Pythagoras and Archimedes. You will learn all about them at school when you're a bit older!
Frank the Postman &

a^2 b^2
a b
c
c^2

Kay the Carrot Top
88 Crooked Moor Road
Brush Hill
Steelfields
England
S10 AWW

We had to take a ferry to reach our sixteenth destination, the island of Cyprus. We visited the town of Paphos where the whole town is a UNESCO heritage site. There is a tree in the city which is supposed to make wishes come true when you tie ribbons and handkerchiefs to its branches. I tied an orange ribbon and wished that we will make it home in time for Christmas. We delivered the parcel to the capital city, Nicosia, where we are staying tonight. They don't like fishing in Cyprus, but they make a tasty cheese called Halloumi, which we ate cooked as kebabs! The official languages are Turkish and Greek, which has its own alphabet! Frank the Postman &

Kourion Ampitheatre, Cyprus

Kay the Carrot Top
88 Crooked Moor Road
Brush Hill
Steelfields
England
S10 AWW

We had to hop back onto a boat to reach our next destination, Malta, a group of islands in the Mediterranean Sea. They drive on the left side of the road as we do in the UK. Most other countries in the world drive on the right! The capital, Valetta, was built in just 15 years in 1566. It's the smallest capital in the EU. We delivered the parcel then drove to Popeye Village and visited Santa's Toy Town. The elves gave Alba White Wolf a squeaky bone gift! Unlike Cyprus, they like to fish here and they paint the fishing boats in bright colours with eyes on the side to protect them from evil spirits! We had a fish platter for dinner with squid, swordfish and octopus! Frank the Postman &

Azure Window, Malta

Kay the Carrot Top
88 Crooked Moor Road
Brush Hill
Steelfields
England
S10 AWW

We sailed back to mainland Europe today and arrived in Italy. It is mountainous and there are three active volcanoes. We delivered the eighteenth star to the capital city, Rome, which has lots of historical architecture, including the Colosseum where Gladiators used to fight! There is also a cat sanctuary in the ancient temple where Julius Caesar was murdered! Alba White Wolf wasn't allowed to visit even though she loves cats! Italians love their food and we've been spoilt with pizza, pasta and gelato ice-cream! In 2007, a dog called Rocco found a truffle worth £165 000 in Pisa! I wonder if Alba White Wolf can find one too?

Frank the Postman &

Tuscany, Italy

Kay the Carrot Top
88 Crooked Moor Road
Brush Hill
Steelfields
England
S10 AWW

We took another ferry from Ancona to Zadar across the Adriatic Sea to reach Croatia, our nineteenth destination. It's a beautiful country with eight national parks and around 1200 islands! We visited the Plitvice Lakes National Park on the way to the capital, Zagreb. The waterfalls were stunningly beautiful, but it was too cold to swim in the lakes at this time of year! We ate a black seafood risotto for dinner which is made with squid ink! Did you know that Dalmatian dogs come from a region in Croatia called Dalmatia! They also invented the neck tie in the 17th century, which your daddy Bill the Accountant still likes to wear every day! Frank the Postman &

Plitvice Lakes National Park, Croatia

Kay the Carrot Top
88 Crooked Moor Road
Brush Hill
Steelfields
England
S10 AWW

Today, we drove to Slovenia and delivered the twentieth star to the capital, Ljubljana. We visited the Dragon Bridge which crosses the Ljubljanica river and saw the impressive dragon statues. We also ate some 'Potica' which is a festive cake with a delicious nut filling. Afterwards, we went to the famous Lipica Stud Farm which breeds beautiful white horses. Alba White Wolf liked them especially because they match her fur. Then we visited the Postojna Cave which is 20km long and we rode on a little railway inside. There are over 10 000 caves in Slovenia. In the Spring they dress up as strange monsters called 'Kurents' for a carnival in Ptuj.

Frank the Postman &

Postojna Caves, Slovenia

Kay the Carrot Top
88 Crooked Moor Road
Brush Hill
Steelfields
England
S10 AWW

We went skiing in the Austrian Alps on our way to the capital of Austria, Vienna. Skiing is the most popular sport in Austria and people come from all over Europe during the winter to stay in the ski resorts. It is also renowned for classical music; Haydn, Schubert, Strauss and Mozart are all famous composers from Austria. In Vienna there are lots of coffee shops and they sell the most delicious cakes! We shared an apple strudel and we attempted to dance a Viennese waltz, but Alba White Wolf wasn't very good! We are hoping to see the traditional 'Krampuslauf' parade of evil monsters that punish naughty children at Christmas! Frank the Postman &

The Alps, Austria

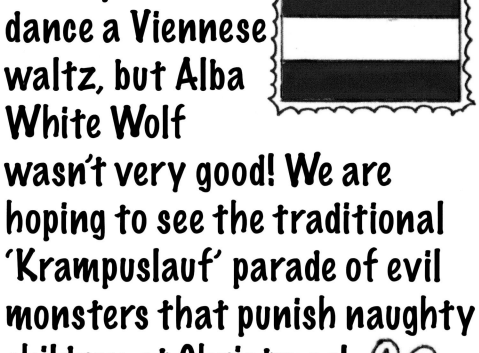

Kay the Carrot Top
88 Crooked Moor Road
Brush Hill
Steelfields
England
S10 AWW

Our twenty-second destination is Berlin, the capital of Germany. There are lots of Christmas markets at this time of year, so we stopped in Leipzig and bought your Christmas presents! We ate some tasty sausages; Alba White Wolf had a Bratwurst and I had a Currywurst which has a spicy sauce. We also bought a Stollen cake to eat on Christmas day. Lots of important inventions came from Germany, including: cars, motorbikes, television, the clarinet, aspirin and gummy bears! A very important scientist called Albert Einstein came from Germany. He received the 1921 Nobel Prize in Physics for his work!

Frank the Postman &

Christmas Market, Germany

$E=mc^2$

Kay the Carrot Top
88 Crooked Moor Road
Brush Hill
Steelfields
England
S10 AWW

ALBA

We made a quick stop in Luxembourg, which is a very small country. Nearly half of the population are foreign born and they speak three languages; Luxembourgish, German and French. The capital is called Luxembourg City. We delivered the twenty-third star to the European Courts of Justice which are in two golden skyscrapers. On the way we stopped at the Schiessentumpel waterfall which is a popular

European Courts of Justice, Luxembourg

tourist spot. We saw a Goldcrest which is their national bird. They seem to like gold things! For lunch we tried the national dish, 'Judd mat Gaardebounen', which is pork, potatoes and beans - very tasty! Frank the Postman &

Kay the Carrot Top
88 Crooked Moor Road
Brush Hill
Steelfields
England
S10 AWW

We sped over the border in the post van to France to deliver the parcel to the capital, Paris. France is the largest country in the EU and called 'L'Hexagone' because of its shape. It's the most visited country in the world. We went up the Eiffel Tower which was built in 1889 and visited the Louvre which is a popular art gallery. Lots of famous artists and writers came from France, including Descartes who said, "Cogito ergo sum". Alba White

Le Mont Sainte Michel, France

Wolf says that means, "I howl, therefore I am." We ate snails, baguette and Roquefort - a very stinky cheese for dinner! I found out that Braille was invented by a French man so blind people can read - how awesome! Frank the Postman &

Kay the Carrot Top
88 Crooked Moor Road
Brush Hill
Steelfields
England
S10 AWW

Our twenty-fifth destination is Spain and we delivered the parcel to the capital, Madrid. They were busy getting ready for Christmas and everybody was buying lottery tickets for 'El Gordo' which means 'the Big One'. We went to a fiesta in our hotel where we played piñata. Alba White Wolf won lots of Chupa-Chubs lollipops but they're not good for her teeth! The name comes from the Spanish word 'chupar' which means 'to suck'!

Art Gallery, Spain

In Catalonia, which is a region of Spain, they have another strange Christmas tradition called 'Tió de Nadal' or 'Pooping Log'! The children feed the log and then it poops out presents! We ate yummy paella with prawns for dinner!
Frank the Postman &

Kay the Carrot Top
88 Crooked Moor Road
Brush Hill
Steelfields
England
S10 AWW

Alba White Wolf had a very exciting journey across the border from Spain to Portugal because she travelled by zip wire! I drove around and collected her in the post van and we travelled to our penultimate destination, Lisbon, the capital of Portugal. On the way we stopped at Porto, where there is an amazing book shop called 'Livraria Lello' and Alba White Wolf found a copy of her book, 'Go Back To Where You Came From!' When we arrived in Lisbon, we drove across the longest bridge in Europe which is 17km and delivered the parcel. I ordered Piri-Piri chicken for lunch; Alba White Wolf didn't want any because it was too spicy!
Frank the Postman &

Kay the Carrot Top
88 Crooked Moor Road
Brush Hill
Steelfields
England
S10 AWW

Livraria Lello Porto, Portugal

We had to abandon the post van and catch a flight to our last country, Ireland. But disaster struck! When we landed in Belfast airport, they told me we were in the capital of Northern Ireland which is part of the UK. I knew we couldn't get to Dublin, the capital of Ireland and make it home in time for Christmas, so we went to the pub and had a pint of Guinness instead. There was a band playing Irish folk tunes and the fiddle player asked me why I was so glum at Christmas. He suggested I try to catch a Leprechaun who would grant 3 wishes or go to the Giant's Causeway and ask the Vikings to take the parcel via the sea. I thought this was the best option!
Frank the Postman &

The Giant's Causeway, Northern Ireland

Kay the Carrot Top
88 Crooked Moor Road
Brush Hill
Steelfields
England
S10 AWW

It was Christmas Eve and Kay the Carrot Top sat looking gloomily out of the window. 'Do you think they will make it home in time for Christmas?' she asked, 'It just won't be the same without them.' 'Let's go to bed, and we'll see in the morning,' her daddy replied.

Kay the Carrot Top woke up on Christmas day when a big, wet tongue started licking her face. 'Hooray! You're home!' she cried and hugged her daddies and Alba White Wolf. 'Merry Christmas!' said Frank the Postman and gave a parcel to Kay the Carrot Top.

'There was one parcel we couldn't deliver because it doesn't have an address,' he said. Kay the Carrot Top unwrapped the 28th parcel and took out the lost star. She thought for a moment before saying, 'I think we should put it on our Christmas tree to keep it safe until we find out who it belongs to.' And that's exactly what they did.

Madeleina Kay is an author, illustrator, singer and political activist. She is passionate about using the arts to challenge damaging cultural attitudes and achieve positive social change. Her books include: 'Go Back To Where You Came from!,' 'Theresa Maybe in Brexitland' and 'Cyril the Ninja Squirrel'. She has recorded singles including: 'Brexit Hokey Cokey' and 'Strong and Stable My Arse' and vocals for the album, 'Rage Against the Brexit Machine'.